Hans-Günter Heumann

Piano Junior

A Creative and Interactive
Piano Course for Children
Theory Book 3

ED 13813

Illustrations by Leopé

Mainz · London · Berlin · Madrid · New York · Paris · Prague · Tokyo · Toronto
© 2017 SCHOTT MUSIC Ltd. London. Printed in Germany

ED 13813
British Library Cataloguing-in-Publication Data.
A catalogue record for this book is available from the British Library
ISMN 979-0-2201-3640-5
ISBN 978-1-84761-430-8

English translation: Schott London Editorial
Design by Barbara Brümmer
Typesetting Barbara Brümmer
Music setting: Darius-Heise-Krzyszton
Cover design: www.adamhaystudio.com
Printed in Germany S&Co. 9208

Contents

Summary of Lesson Book 3

Intervals

Sixth   Seventh   Octave

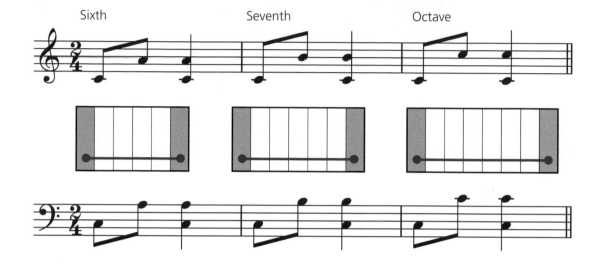

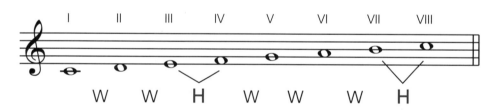

Musical Terms	• espressivo / espr.	• Opus / Op.	• Metronome
	• grazioso	• Sequence	• Right Pedal
	• non troppo	• simile / sim.	

Scales

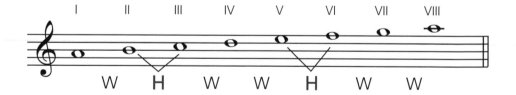

C Major Scale

W   W   H   W   W   W   H

Natural A Minor Scale

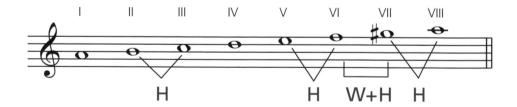

W   H   W   W   H   W   W

Harmonic A Minor Scale

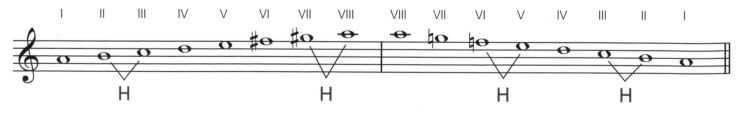

H   H   W+H   H

Melodic A Minor Scale

H   H   H   H

4

C Major Triad/Chord

Primary Chords in C Major

C   F   G

I   IV   V

C Major Triad with Inversions

C

Root position   1st inversion   2nd inversion

Dominant Seventh Chord in C Major

G^7 G^7

V7   1st inversion without fifth

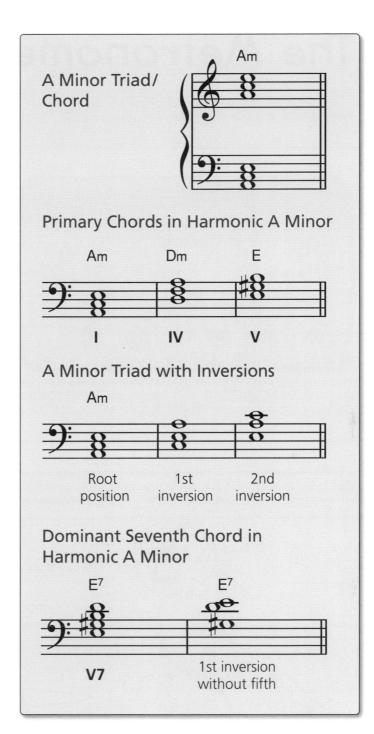

A Minor Triad/Chord

Primary Chords in Harmonic A Minor

Am   Dm   E

I   IV   V

A Minor Triad with Inversions

Am

Root position   1st inversion   2nd inversion

Dominant Seventh Chord in Harmonic A Minor

E^7 E^7

V7   1st inversion without fifth

Range of Book 3

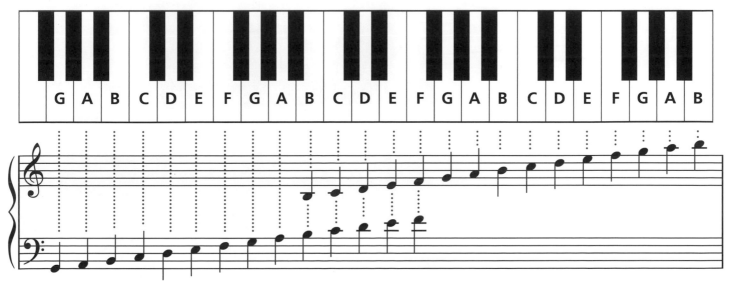

The Metronome

The metronome is a kind of musical clock that can be used to check the tempo of a piece of music. Mechanical and electronic devices are available – and you can download a metronome app, too.

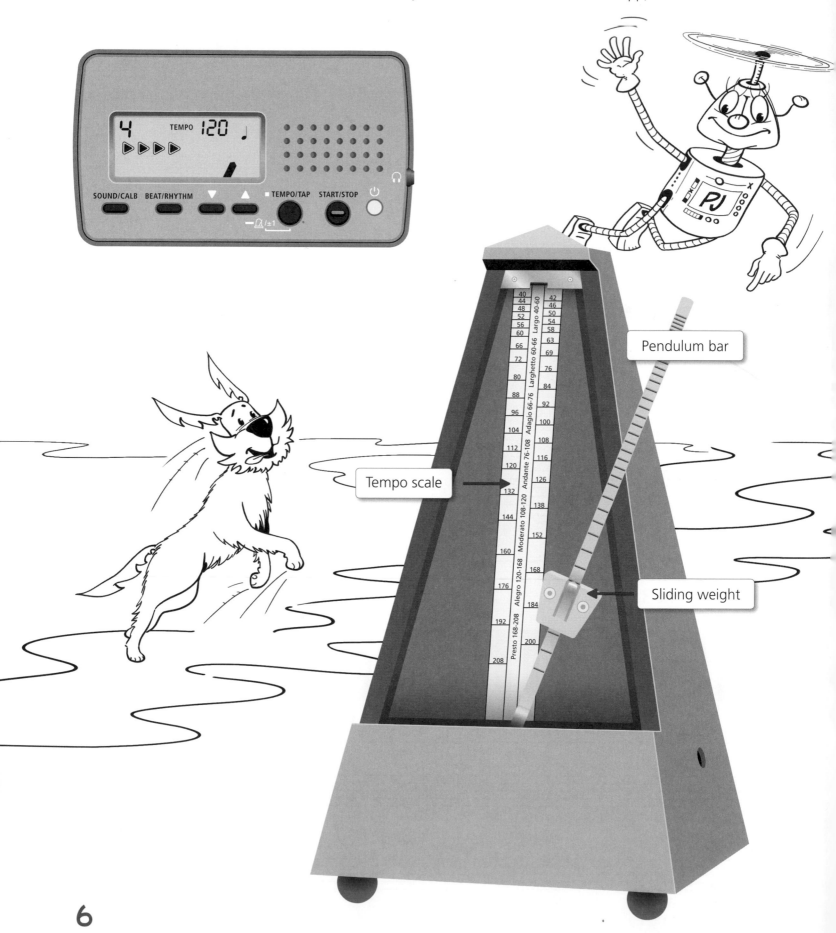

Pendulum bar

Tempo scale

Sliding weight

Before using a mechanical metronome you have to wind it up like a clock. Then you can start!

Metronome markings are given at the beginning of a piece, for example: ♩ = 100 means **100 crotchet/quarter note beats per minute.**

The speeds on a metronome range from 40 to 208 beats per minute. Well-known musicians such as Ludwig van Beethoven wished for a means of measuring precise tempos for their musical compositions. The metronome invented by **Johann Nepomuk Mälzel** (1772-1838) was used increasingly from 1816 onwards. Mälzel also developed several ear trumpets for Beethoven, who was hard of hearing.

ACTION CORNER

Shift the weight on the pendulum up and down the tempo scale and keep the metronome ticking. At 40 you will hear a very slow beat, while 208 is very fast.

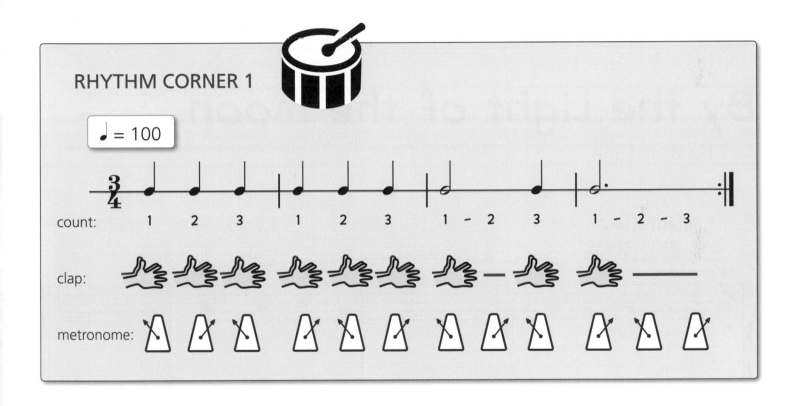

Changing Fingers on the Same Key

COMPOSING CORNER 1

Play BY THE LIGHT OF THE MOON in 3/4 time (see p. 9, example 1) and in 2/4 time (see p. 9, example 2). Write out these two examples in musical notation, too.

Then add tempo indications, metronome markings, bar lines, repeat marks, double bars, fingerings, dynamics and phrase marks.

Try playing the entire piece a whole tone lower.

By the Light of the Moon

Au Clair de la Lune

By the Light of the Moon

Au Clair de la Lune

Fine

D. C. al Fine

By the Light of the Moon

Au Clair de la Lune

Fine

D.C. al Fine

Spreading Your Fingers

Exercise 1:

Place your RH in position with the thumb over middle C.
Close your eyes and play middle C as a minim/half note with your thumb.
Now reach out with your 2nd finger to play the note E on the 3rd beat. To find the note E,
slide your finger silently across the D to E.

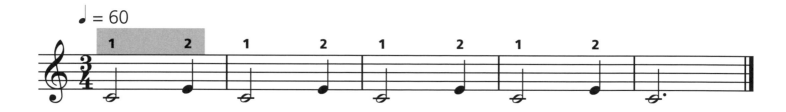

Exercise 2:

Begin as in Exercise 1.
Now reach out with your 3rd finger to play the note F on the 3rd beat. To find the note F,
slide your finger silently across from E to F.

10

Exercise 3:

Begin as in Exercise 1.
Now reach out with your 4th finger to play the note G on the 3rd beat. To find the note G, slide your finger silently across from F to G.

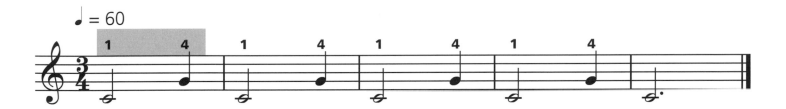

Exercise 4:

Begin as in Exercise 1.
Now reach out with your 5th finger to play the note A on the 3rd beat. To find the note A, slide your finger silently across from G to A.

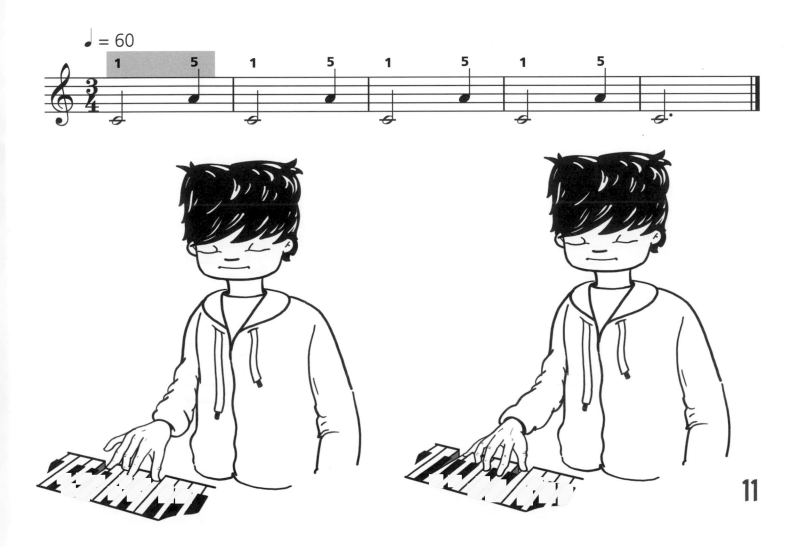

Intervals and Notation: Sixths

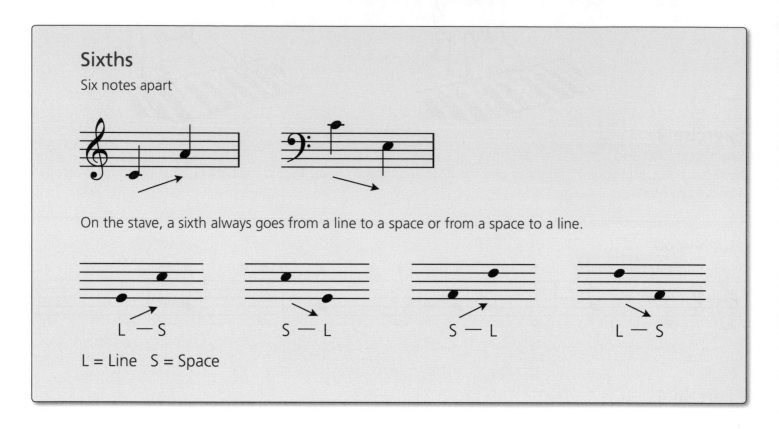

Sixths

Six notes apart

On the stave, a sixth always goes from a line to a space or from a space to a line.

L — S   S — L   S — L   L — S

L = Line   S = Space

Finding Sixths

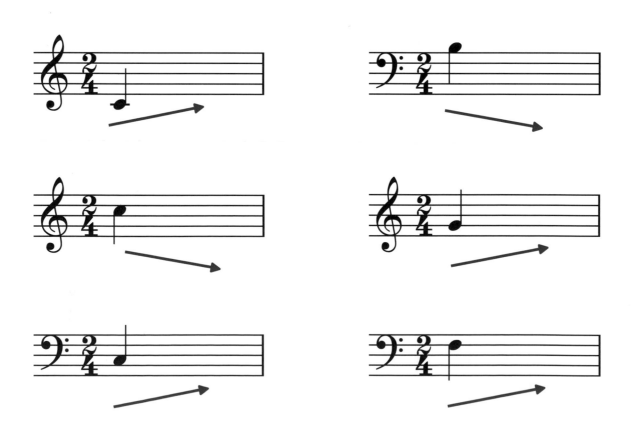

Write in the missing parts of the melody to this SIXTHS WALTZ: it always goes in sixths above the lower RH part. Then play this piece from memory.

COMPOSING CORNER 2

Sixths Waltz

HGH & ....
Fill in your name

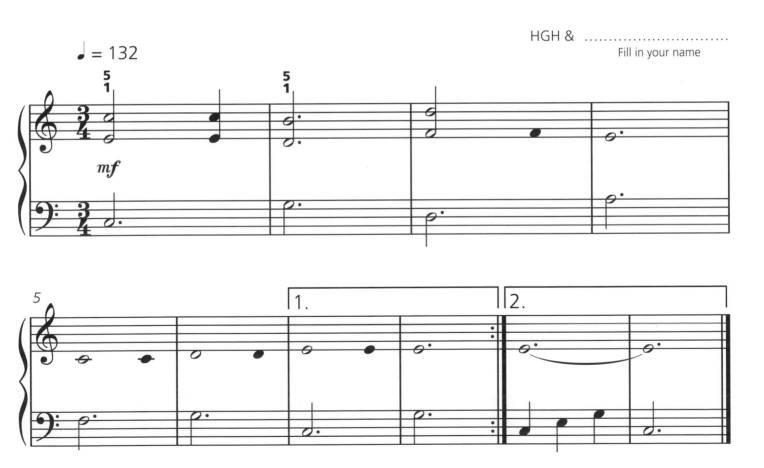

Funny Bird

HGH

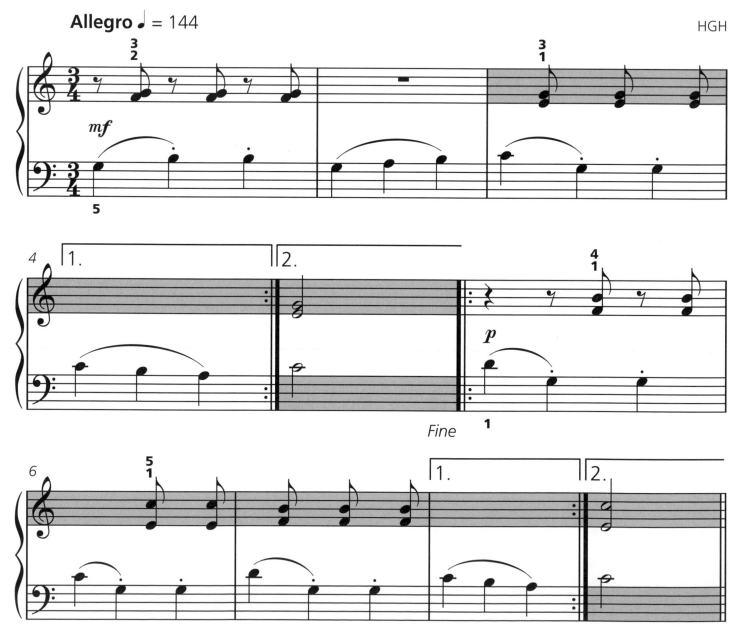

Fine

D. C. al Fine
with repetition

Tricky Memory Game

MEMORY CORNER

Your teacher will play you each of these four musical examples slowly three times. When you have listened and watched carefully, it's your turn to play the first example – GOOD NEWS – as well as you can from memory. If you can do that, move on to the second example; if not, your teacher will play example 1 again for you.

Good News

Sad News

Squirrel Playing

What a Lovely Day

Extending the Range of Notes in RH

Copy Everything I Do

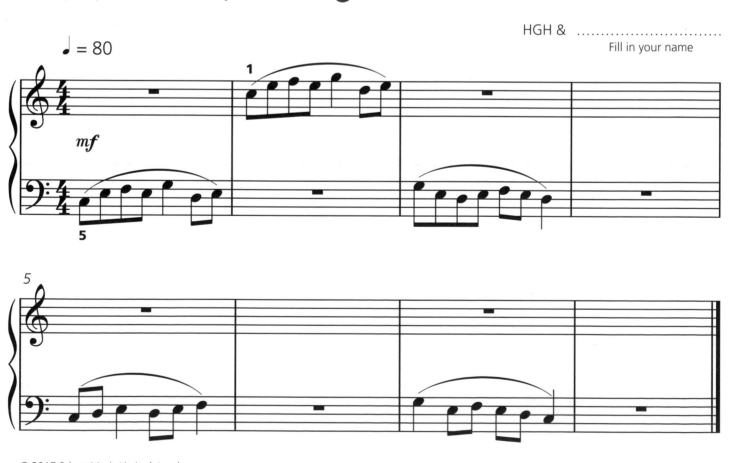

HGH & ....
Fill in your name

Draw a picture

Be Creative

COMPOSING CORNER 5

Give this piece a suitable name.
Then write in tempo/metronome markings,
dynamics, phrasing and fingerings.
Draw an imaginative picture to go with the piece.

....

Title of the piece

....

Metronome markings

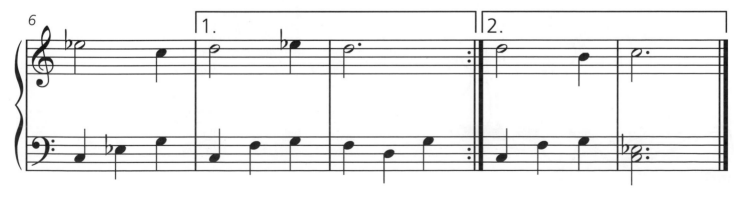

Sequence Teardrops

HGH & ....
Fill in your name

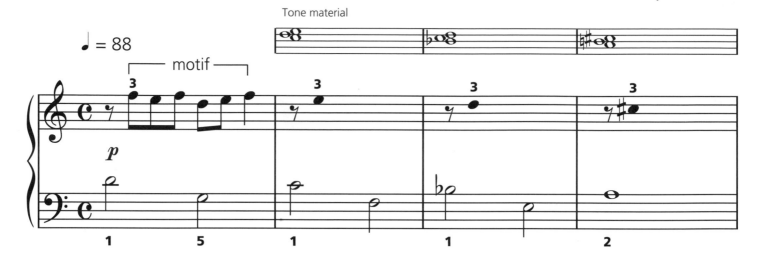

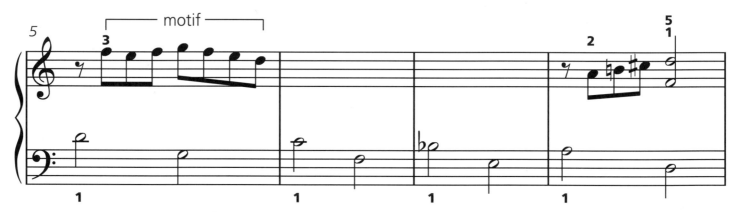

COMPOSING CORNER 6

Compose the melody to TEARDROPS, continuing the sequence as indicated in bars/measures 1, 5, 9, 13, 17 and 21 – and write the notes on the stave.

Notes are not given for LH either from bar 9 onwards: you will have to copy the notes from bars 1-8 twice more. Have fun!

Play this piece from memory.

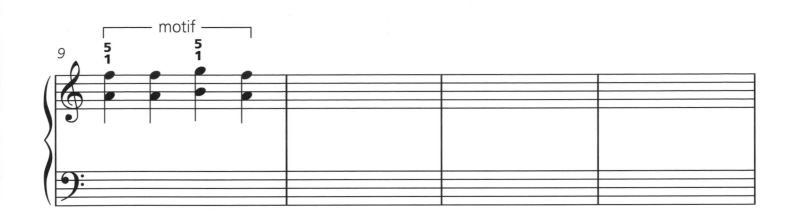

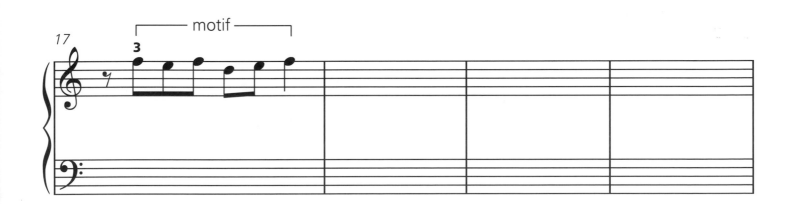

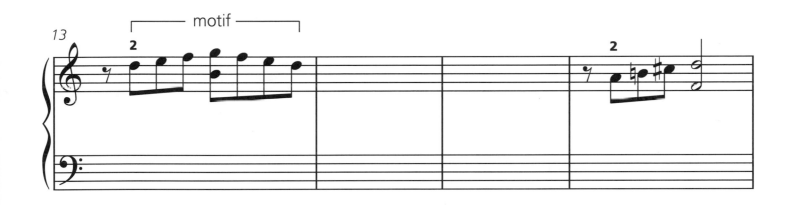

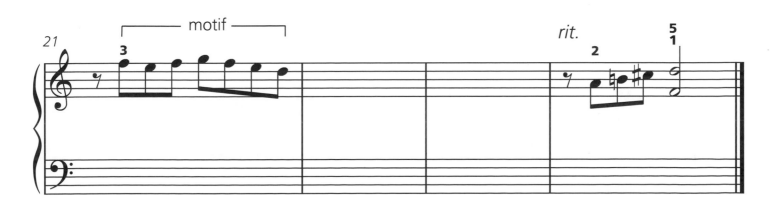

Intervals and Notation: Sevenths

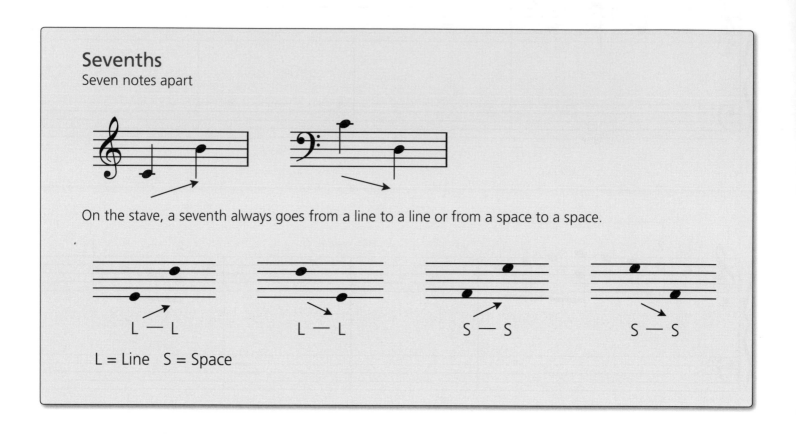

Sevenths
Seven notes apart

On the stave, a seventh always goes from a line to a line or from a space to a space.

L — L   L — L   S — S   S — S

L = Line   S = Space

Finding Sevenths

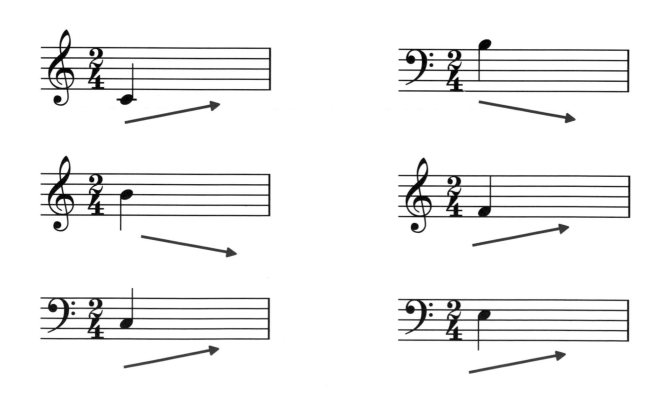

Spanish Guitar

Intervals and Notation: Octaves

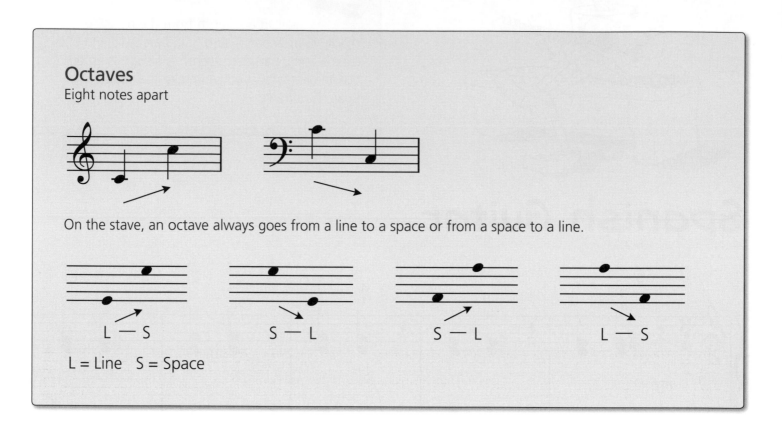

Octaves
Eight notes apart

On the stave, an octave always goes from a line to a space or from a space to a line.

L — S   S — L   S — L   L — S

L = Line   S = Space

Finding Octaves

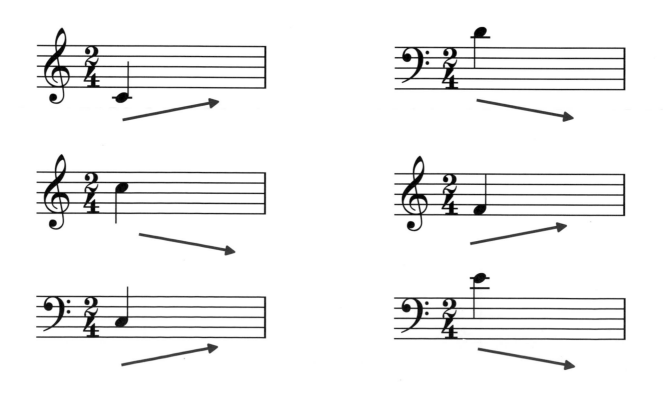

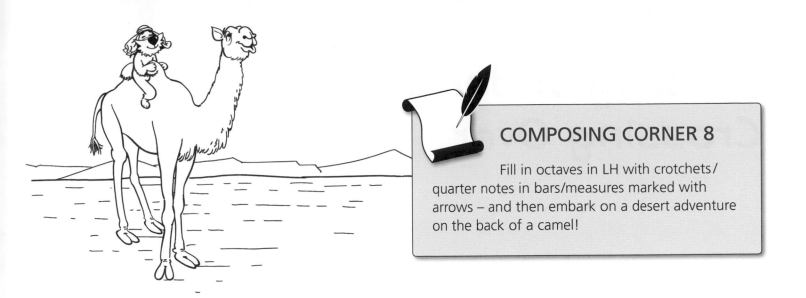

COMPOSING CORNER 8

Fill in octaves in LH with crotchets / quarter notes in bars/measures marked with arrows – and then embark on a desert adventure on the back of a camel!

The Caravan in the Desert

HGH & ....
Fill in your name

Passing Under and Crossing Over

1. Hold down the 1st note in a group of two black notes with your 2nd finger and play the two adjacent white notes (C + D) with your thumb. Let your hand move gently sideways without lifting the wrist, with the thumb moving independently. Play each exercise eight times.

RH

2. Hold down the 2nd note in a group of two black notes with your 3rd finger and play the two adjacent white notes (D + E) with your thumb.

RH

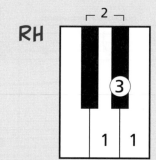

3. Hold down the 1st note in a group of two black notes with your 3rd finger and play the two adjacent white notes (C + D) with your thumb.

LH

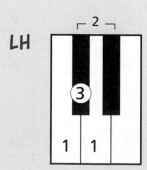

24

4. Hold down the 2nd note in a group of two black notes with your 2nd finger and play the two adjacent white notes (D + E) with your thumb.

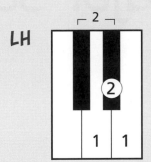

5. Hold down the 1st note in a group of three black notes with your 2nd finger and play the two adjacent white notes (F + G) with your thumb.

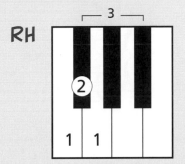

6. Hold down the 2nd note in a group of three black notes with your 3rd finger and play the two adjacent white notes (G + A) with your thumb.

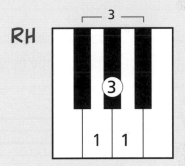

7. Hold down the 3rd note in a group of three black notes with your 4th finger and play the two adjacent white notes (A + B) with your thumb.

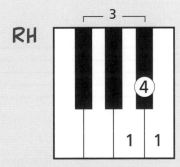

8. Now play exercises 5-7 with your LH on a group of three black notes. Notice the correct fingering.

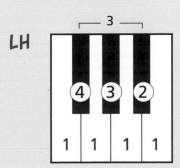

C Major Scale

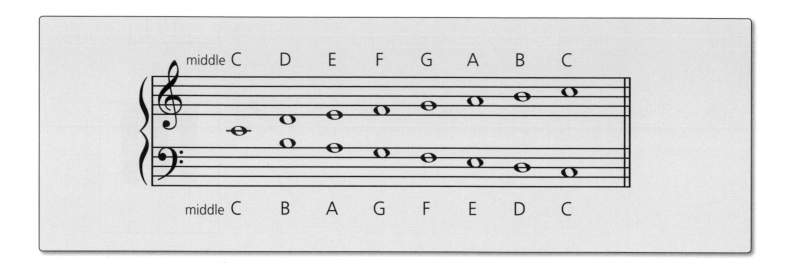

Write the scale of C major in the treble clef, going upwards in semibreves/whole notes.

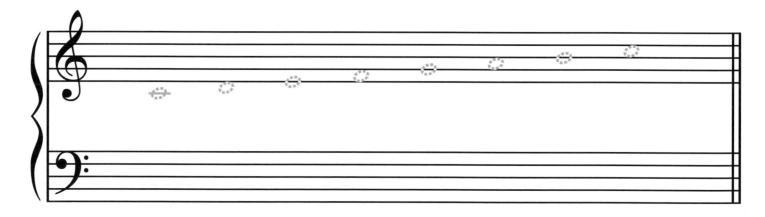

Write the scale of C major in the bass clef, going downwards in semibreves/whole notes.

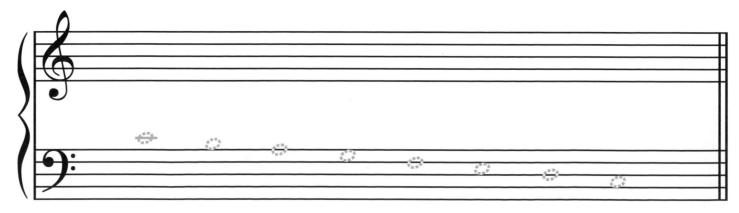

C Major Scale Pyramid

Write out all the notes of the scale that you can see on the pyramid, one after another in crotchets/quarter notes, up and down on the stave.

Interval Recognition

EAR TRAINING CORNER 1

Your teacher will play these melodic and harmonic intervals to you on the piano in any order. First just listen closely, then sing along, then sing those intervals without piano accompaniment and name them. Try to measure large intervals step by step.

Listening Test

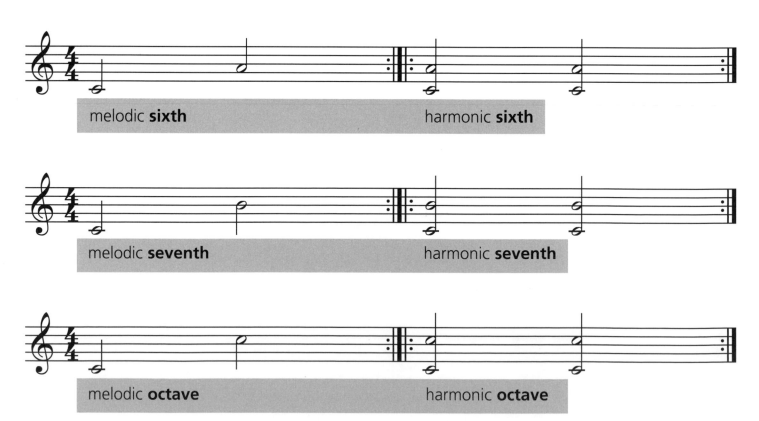

melodic **sixth**   harmonic **sixth**

melodic **seventh**   harmonic **seventh**

melodic **octave**   harmonic **octave**

Singing Exercises

Start by playing the first note of the exercise. Then sing each phrase in one breath. Now play the same thing on the piano, with the same singing *legato* tone. This is called **playing cantabile** (= singing tone) on the piano.

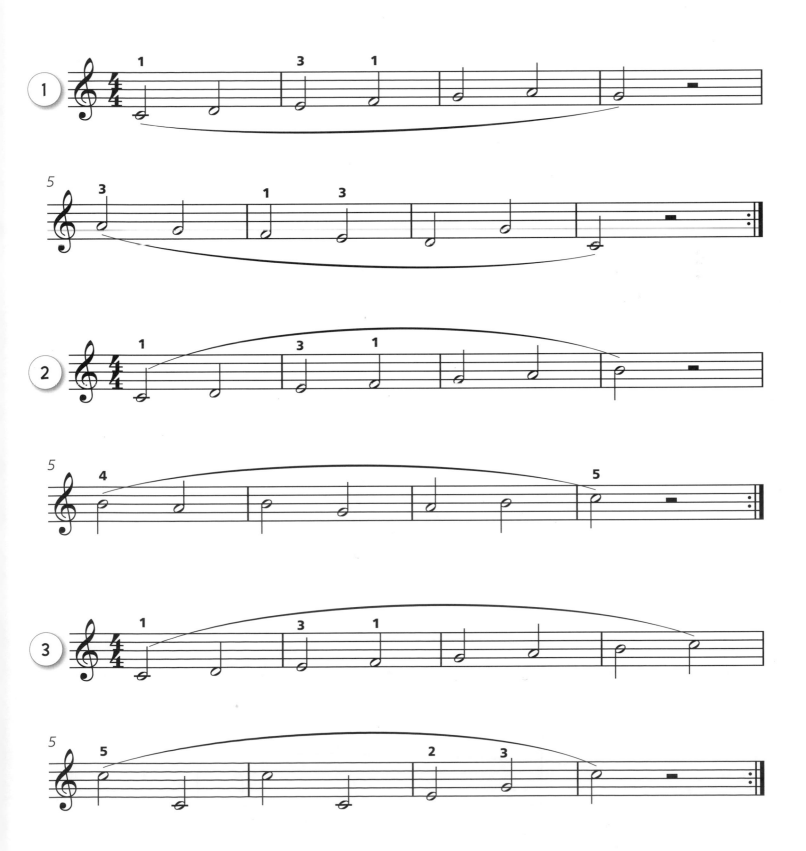

Sight-Reading

Sight-Reading Pieces

HGH

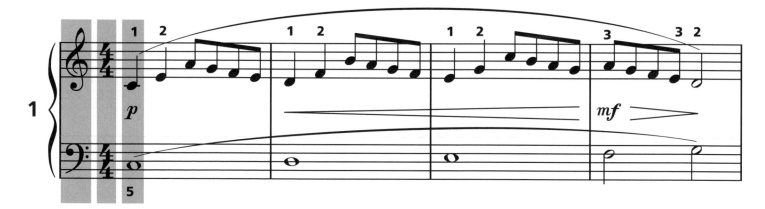

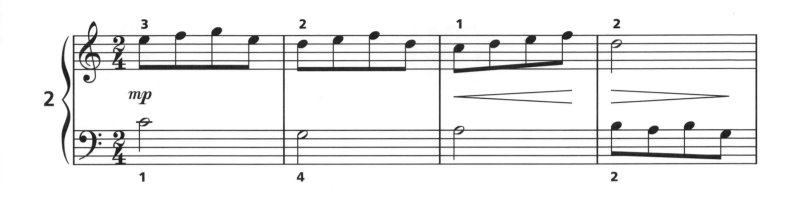

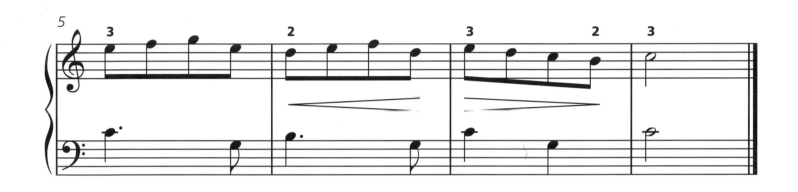

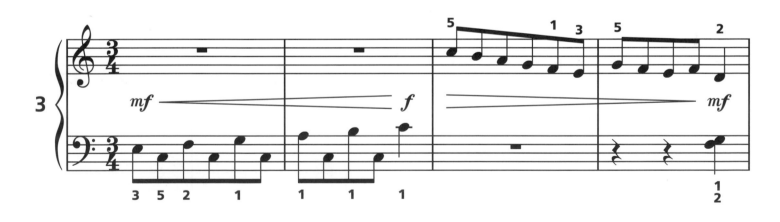

C Major Chord

Row, Row, Row Your Boat

♩. = 60

Children's Song from the USA
Arr.: HGH

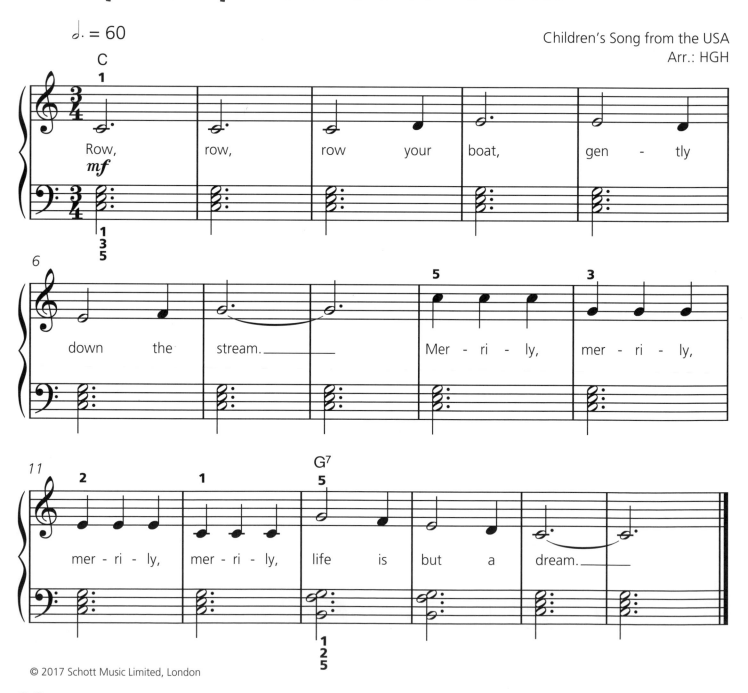

© 2017 Schott Music Limited, London

Play the piece from page 32 with the following two kinds of accompaniment. Transpose this children's song into D, too, a whole tone higher. Make sure you use a black note here, F♯.

Accompaniment patterns

Transposing one whole tone / whole step higher

Accompaniment patterns

33

Natural A Minor Scale

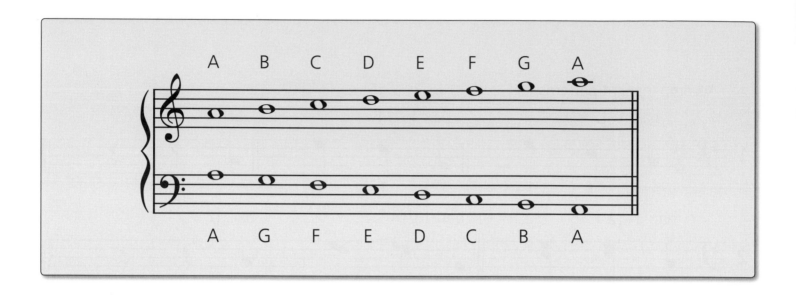

Write the natural A minor scale in the treble clef going upwards in semibreves/whole notes.

Write the natural A minor scale in the bass clef going downwards in semibreves/whole notes.

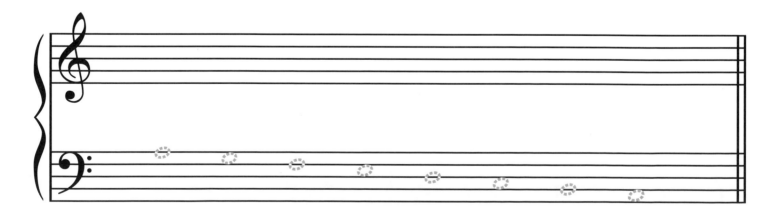

Scale and Chord Exercises

EAR TRAINING CORNER 2

Your teacher will play scales and chords for you on the piano in any order. You have to decide whether you hear a major or minor scale, or a major or minor chord. First listen carefully, then sing along and say what you have heard. Remember that major sounds bright, clear and happy, while minor sounds dark, gloomy and sad. With any aural exercises, try to imagine how the notes should sound.

Major or Minor Scale?

Major or Minor Chord?

Name these Notes

Harmonic A Minor Scale

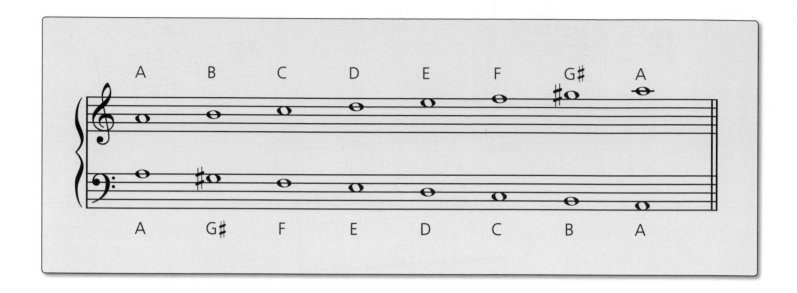

Write the harmonic A minor scale in the treble clef going upwards in semibreves/whole notes.

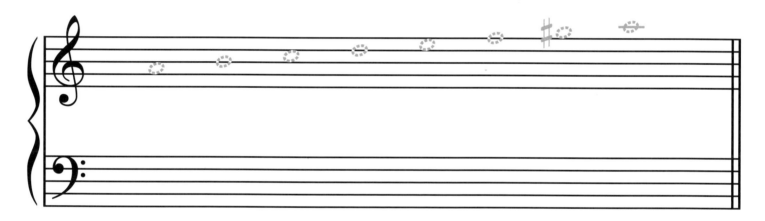

Write the harmonic A minor scale in the bass clef going downwards in semibreves/whole notes.

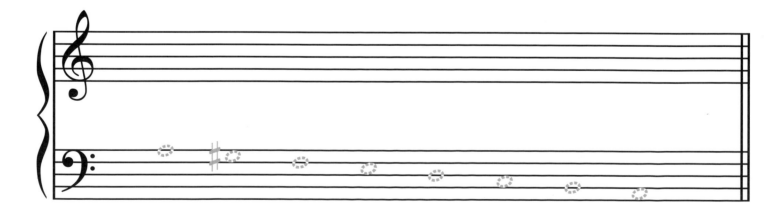

Melodic A Minor Scale

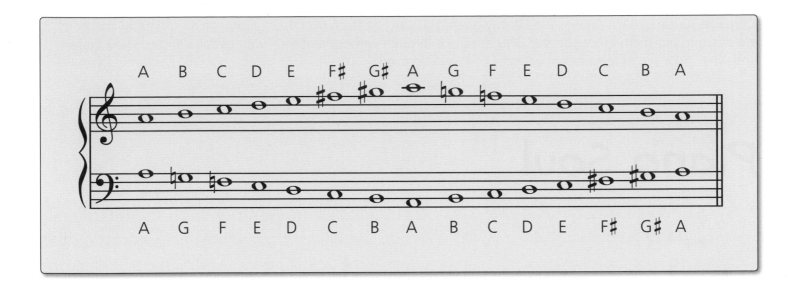

Write the melodic A minor scale in the treble clef going up and down in semibreves / whole notes.

Write the melodic A minor scale in the bass clef going down and up in semibreves / whole notes.

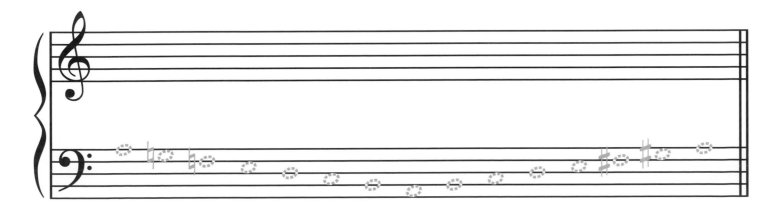

The Right Pedal

On page 40 the pedal markings are already given: you can just trace over them. On page 41 the pedal markings are missing: put them in for yourself. Play the piece through without and then with pedal: which do you prefer and why? Your piano teacher will want to hear your answer!

Piano Soul

HGH

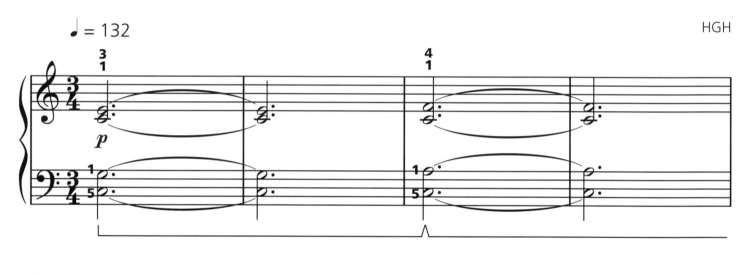

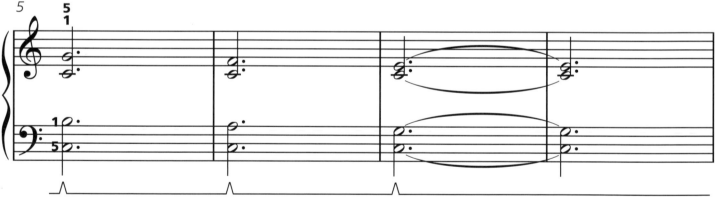

Composing a Piano Piece with Pedal

COMPOSING CORNER 9

Here you'll find the beginning of a piano piece that you can finish yourself: the bass part is already written out. You'll have to write a melody using the notes and rhythms given (in small print above the treble stave). Then think of a suitable title for the piece, adding metronome markings, dynamics, articulation, fingering – and of course your name as composer. Now the piece is ready to play: congratulations!

....

Title of the piece

....

Metronome markings   Fill in your name

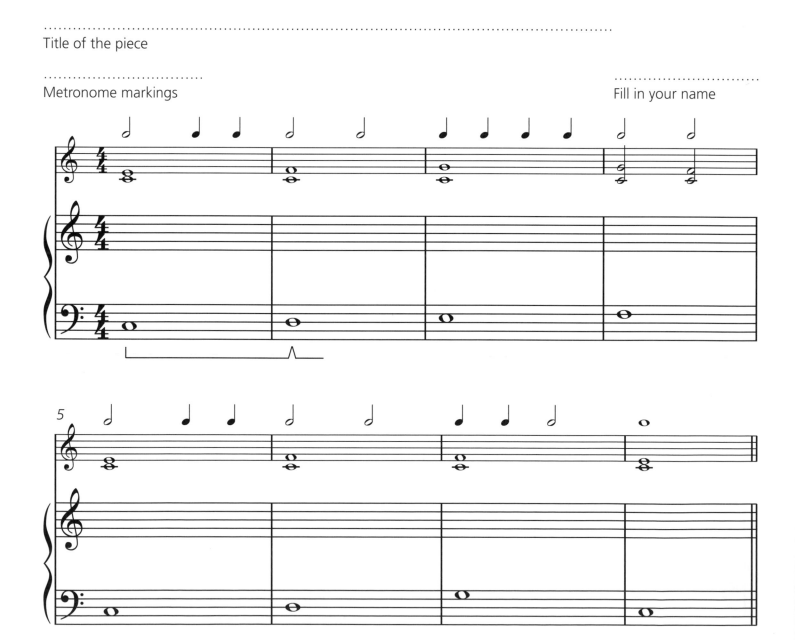

Fine

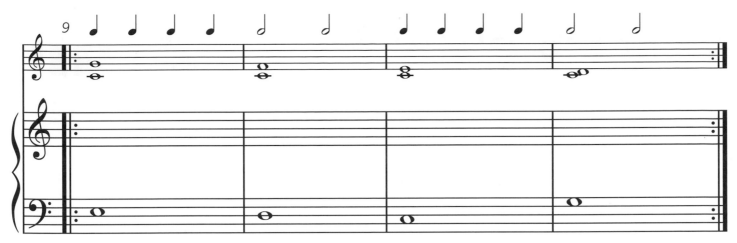

D. C. al Fine

Draw a lovely picture to go with your composition

Clapping Rhythms

RHYTHM
CORNER 2

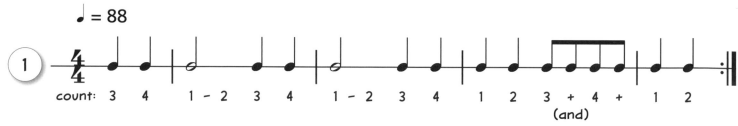

Piano Junior Quiz

1. What is the name for a polyphonic piece of music where all parts play the same tune, one after another?

- [ ] a) minuet
- [ ] b) canon
- [ ] c) waltz

2. What do we call an interval six notes apart?

- [ ] a) a seventh
- [ ] b) a second
- [ ] c) a sixth

3. What does espressivo mean?

- [ ] a) fast
- [ ] b) expressive
- [ ] c) slow

4. What is a sequence?

- [ ] a) repeating a pattern of notes from the same starting point
- [ ] b) repeating a pattern of notes from different starting points
- [ ] c) repeating one note several times

5. What is an octave?

- [ ] a) an interval 6 notes apart
- [ ] b) an interval 7 notes apart
- [ ] c) an interval 8 notes apart

6. How does a major key sound?

☐ a) dark, gloomy, sad
☐ b) bright, clear, happy

7. Where are the semitone steps in a major scale?

☐ a) between 2nd – 3rd and 5th – 6th notes
☐ b) between 3rd – 4th and 7th – 8th notes
☐ c) between 4th – 5th and 7th – 8th notes

8. A minor key is characterized by the sound of the minor third. This interval consists of:

☐ a) 3 semitone steps
☐ b) 4 semitone steps
☐ c) 3 whole tone steps

9. Which notes in the minor scale make up a minor triad?

☐ a) 1st, 3rd & 5th notes
☐ b) 2nd, 4th & 6th notes
☐ c) 3rd, 5th & 7th notes

10. The right pedal, also called the sustaining pedal, is normally applied

☐ a) before notes are played
☐ b) when notes are played
☐ c) after notes are played

Solutions: 1b, 2c, 3b, 4b, 5c, 6b, 7b, 8a, 9a, 10c